THE ANDY CAPP ANNUAL

ISBN: 9781848568754

PUBLISHED BY TITAN BOOKS
A DIVISION OF TITAN PUBLISHING GROUP LTD.
144 SOUTHWARK ST.
LONDON
SE1 0UP

ANDY CAPP IS WRITTEN BY ROGER KETTLE
AND DRAWN BY ROGER MAHONEY.

A CIP CATALOGUE RECORD FOR THIS TITLE IS AVAILABLE FROM THE BRITISH LIBRARY.

FIRST EDITION: SEPTEMBER 2010

10 9 8 7 6 5 4 3 2 1

PRINTED IN ITALY.

WHAT DID YOU THINK OF THIS BOOK? WE LOVE TO HEAR FROM OUR READERS. PLEASE EMAIL US AT: READERFEEDBACK@TITANEMAIL.COM, OR WRITE TO US AT THE ABOVE ADDRESS.

TO RECEIVE ADVANCE INFORMATION, NEWS, COMPETITIONS, AND EXCLUSIVE OFFERS ONLINE, PLEASE SIGN UP FOR THE TITAN NEWSLETTER ON OUR WEBSITE: WWW.TITANBOOKS.COM

MUCH OF THE COMIC STRIP SOURCE MATERIAL USED BY TITAN BOOKS IN THIS EDITION IS EXCEEDINGLY RARE. AS SUCH, WE HOPE THAT READERS CAN APPRECIATE THAT THE QUALITY OF REPRODUCTION ACHIEVABLE CAN VARY.

ANDY CAPP

ANNUAL

TITAN BOOKS

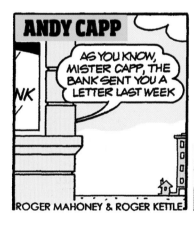

ANDY CAPP

ROGER MAHONEY & ROGER KETTLE

ANDY CAPP

ROGER MAHONEY & ROGER KETTLE

ANDY CAPP

ROGER MAHONEY & ROGER KETTLE

ANDY CAPP

ROGER MAHONEY & ROGER KETTLE

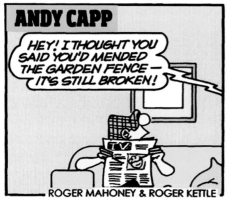

ANDY CAPP

THEY WON TWO-NIL AND HE SCORED BOTH GOALS

ANY SECOND NOW, WE'LL GET THE MODEST APPRAISAL OF HIS PERFORMANCE

WHAT'S A GOOD WORD FOR "MAGNIFICENT" AND "BRILLIANT"? MAGNILLIANT? BRILLIFICENT?

ROGER MAHONEY & ROGER KETTLE

ANDY CAPP

YOU KNOW, SWANS ARE A LOT LIKE PEOPLE — THEY PICK A MATE FOR LIFE...

ROGER MAHONEY & ROGER KETTLE

...AND SETTLE FOR A MISERABLE EXISTENCE JUST LIKE US

ANDY CAPP

ANY CHANCE OF SOME FOOD IN HERE?

ROGER MAHONEY & ROGER KETTLE

IGNORE HIM, RUBE — HE'S IN A BAD MOOD

HE SLEPT IN THIS MORNING AND MISSED HIS ELEVEN O'CLOCK NAP

ANDY CAPP

HI, I'M ANDY — WELCOME TO THE NEIGHBOURHOOD

ROGER MAHONEY & ROGER KETTLE

I MOVED IN THREE YEARS AGO — IT'S STRANGE THAT YOU SHOULD CHOOSE THIS MOMENT TO INTRODUCE YOURSELF...

...TEN MINUTES AFTER I HAD TWO CRATES OF BEER DELIVERED

REALLY? I HADN'T NOTICED

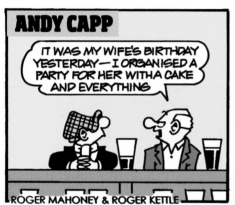

ANDY CAPP

GOOD LUCK — CATCH LOTS OF FISH

THANKS, PET

NOW LET ME THINK... RIVER ...CANAL ...RESERVOIR...

...WHICH ONE WILL I PRETEND TO HAVE BEEN AT WHEN I GET HOME?

ROGER MAHONEY & ROGER KETTLE

ANDY CAPP

'EVENING, VICAR — FANCY A QUICK DRINK?

WELL, A SMALL SHERRY BEFORE DINNER WOULD BE NICE BUT I DIDN'T TAKE ANY MONEY OUT WITH ME

OH, DON'T WORRY ABOUT THAT!

I'M SURE THEY'LL ACCEPT AN I.O.U. FROM YOU

ROGER MAHONEY & ROGER KETTLE

ANDY CAPP

IS THAT YOUR MUM GOING INTO THE BINGO?

YES, SHE'S WEARING HER OLD FUR COAT AND HAT

WHAT WE NEED NOW IS A SHORT-SIGHTED GAME WARDEN WITH A TRANQUILISER GUN

ROGER MAHONEY & ROGER KETTLE

ANDY CAPP

HI, ANDY — WE'RE HAVING A BIT OF A PLUMBING CRISIS AT OUR PLACE

HAVE YOU GOT ANYTHING I COULD USE TO UNBLOCK A DRAIN?

YES, BUT SHE'S AT WORK

ROGER MAHONEY & ROGER KETTLE

ANDY CAPP

SO HOW DID THE WEIGH-IN AT YOUR SLIMMING CLASS GO?

HOW DID BEING STUPID WITH A STUPID NEWSPAPER ON A STUPID COUCH GO?

I'M GUESSING THE SCALES WERE NOT HER FRIEND TONIGHT

ROGER MAHONEY & ROGER KETTLE

ANDY CAPP

THE SIMPLE FACT IS THAT WOMEN ARE BETTER AT MULTI-TASKING THAN MEN

I HAVE TO AGREE WITH YOU – TAKE MY FLO, FOR EXAMPLE...

...SHE CAN BE LOUD, ANNOYING AND WRONG ALL AT THE SAME TIME

ROGER MAHONEY & ROGER KETTLE

ANDY CAPP

"MEN WANTED FOR DANGEROUS BUT HIGHLY PAID CONSTRUCTION WORK"

"TOP WAGES WILL BE ON OFFER TO SUCCESSFUL APPLICANTS"

NAH! EVEN WITH A FALSE BEARD, SHE PROBABLY WOULDN'T GO FOR IT

ROGER MAHONEY & ROGER KETTLE

ANDY CAPP

SO HOW WAS THAT WEDDING YOU AND ANDY WENT TO?

TERRIBLE

AS IS USUAL DURING THE CEREMONY, THE VICAR ASKED IF THERE WERE ANY OBJECTIONS TO THE MARRIAGE

GUESS WHO SHOUTED "WELL, THEY'RE BOTH UGLY BUT FIRE AWAY"?

ROGER MAHONEY & ROGER KETTLE

ANDY CAPP

NEARLY ALL THE RECIPES I COOK WITH ARE MY MOTHER'S OR MY GRANDMOTHER'S

I SHOULD COLLECT THEM ALL TOGETHER AND PUT THEM IN A BOOK

YOU COULD CALL IT "RUINING FOOD— THREE GENERATIONS EXPLAIN HOW"

ROGER MAHONEY & ROGER KETTLE

ANDY CAPP

I'LL NEED A PHONEBOOK, A PEN, SOME WRITING PAPER...

I SENSE A CAMPAIGN COMING ON

BEER PRICES SET TO SOAR

ROGER MAHONEY & ROGER KETTLE

ANDY CAPP

DIDN'T WE HAVE A DRINK IN THAT PUB ONCE?

FIVE YEARS AGO

THE BARMAN WAS CALLED JOHN, THEY HAD FOURTEEN DRAUGHT BEERS ON OFFER AND THREE POOL TABLES

YET TRY ASKING HIM WHEN MY BIRTHDAY IS

ROGER MAHONEY & ROGER KETTLE

ANDY CAPP

THE TROUBLE WITH THAT HUSBAND OF YOURS IS—

SHH, MUM— ANDY'S IN THE LIVING ROOM

OKAY, I'LL TALK IN CODE SO HE DOESN'T UNDERSTAND...

...SLOB LAZY A IS YOURS OF HUSBAND THAT

ROGER MAHONEY & ROGER KETTLE

ANDY CAPP

I'LL COME BACK TO YOU WHEN YOU GET YOUR PRIORITIES RIGHT!

DON'T LEAVE, PET, YOU'LL ALWAYS BE MY— GOAL! YOU BEAUTY! —NUMBER ONE WHATSIT

ROGER MAHONEY & ROGER KETTLE

ANDY CAPP

WELL? HOW DID YOUR REQUEST FOR A LOAN GO AT THE BANK?

ROGER MAHONEY & ROGER KETTLE

THEY ASKED ME TO PUT MY APPLICATION IN WRITING

THAT'S A GOOD SIGN!

NOT REALLY— THEY LIKE TO READ OUT THE FUNNIEST ONES AT THEIR CHRISTMAS PARTY

ANDY CAPP

I'M TRYING TO WORK OUT THIS SECRET SYSTEM OF YOURS

ROGER MAHONEY & ROGER KETTLE

IS IT "PLACE BET, WATCH HORSE LOSE, TEAR UP TICKET AND SWEAR"?

YOU'RE NOT HELPING

ANDY CAPP

REMEMBER WE'RE GOING TO MY MUM'S FOR DINNER TONIGHT

ROGER MAHONEY & ROGER KETTLE

SEVEN FOR SEVEN-THIRTY

WHEN DO WE HAVE TO BE THERE?

I PRESUME THAT GIVES HER THIRTY MINUTES TIN-OPENING TIME

ROGER MAHONEY & ROGER KETTLE

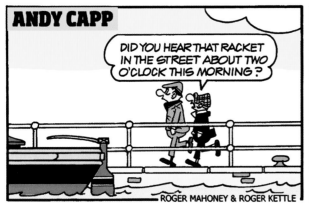

ANDY CAPP

...AND THAT WAS WHEN MY MOTHER TRIPPED ON THE PAVEMENT AND FELL OVER

YOUR MOTHER? I'D HEARD IT WAS ANDY WHO'D HURT HIS BACK

IT WAS — HE PULLED A MUSCLE, LAUGHING

ROGER MAHONEY & ROGER KETTLE

ANDY CAPP

SO DID ANDY GET YOU A PRESENT FOR YOUR ANNIVERSARY?

HALF A DOZEN

THAT'S GREAT!

NOT REALLY,— IT WAS A SIX-PACK OF BEER

ROGER MAHONEY & ROGER KETTLE

ANDY CAPP

HI, UNCLE ANDY— DID YOU HEAR I GOT ENGAGED LAST WEEK?

INDEED I DID

WELL, I CAN'T STOP — I PROMISED WENDY I'D GO LATE-NIGHT SHOPPING WITH HER

AND SO IT BEGINS, JACK, SO IT BEGINS

I'LL GET YOU A BEER

ROGER MAHONEY & ROGER KETTLE

ANDY CAPP

YOU *COULD* HELP ME WITH THESE SHOPPING BAGS, Y'KNOW

SUPERMARKET

I CAN'T, PET— I'VE GOT A DARTS MATCH TONIGHT AND I DON'T WANT TO STRAIN MY THROWING HAND

WOULD YOU LIKE TO SEE ME STRAIN MY *SLAPPING* HAND?

PERHAPS I COULD MANAGE ONE

ROGER MAHONEY & ROGER KETTLE

ANDY CAPP

HANG ON A SECOND, RUBE — I NEED TO BUY ANDY A NEW PAIR OF WORK TROUSERS

"WORK" TROUSERS?

ROGER MAHONEY & ROGER KETTLE

THEY HAVE TO HAVE A SMALL CONCEALED POCKET FOR HIS POOL CHALK

ANDY CAPP

STILL LOOKING THROUGH THE JOB VACANCIES?

YES...

BUT I'VE NARROWED IT DOWN TO A COUPLE OF POSSIBILITIES

GOOD FOR YOU, PET

SO WHICH TWO ARE YOU GOING TO PRETEND TO APPLY FOR?

ROGER MAHONEY & ROGER KETTLE

ANDY CAPP

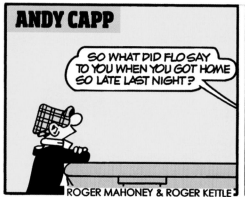

SO WHAT DID FLO SAY TO YOU WHEN YOU GOT HOME SO LATE LAST NIGHT?

ROGER MAHONEY & ROGER KETTLE

"OH, YOU"

THAT'S ALL?

I'VE EDITED OUT THE SWEARING FROM A TWENTY-MINUTE MONOLOGUE

ANDY CAPP

EXCUSE ME, THIS DRESS DOESN'T HAVE A PRICE TAG ON IT — HOW MUCH IS IT?

TWO HUNDRED AND FIFTY POUNDS

ROGER MAHONEY & ROGER KETTLE

AND IF YOU STICK IT IN YOUR MOUTH TO STIFLE A SCREAM, YOU'LL HAVE TO PAY FOR IT

ANDY CAPP

SAME AGAIN, ANDY?

I CAN'T—I'VE GOT WORK IN THE MORNING

ROGER MAHONEY & ROGER KETTLE

HEH! HEH! HEH! HEH! HEH! HEH! HEH!

THAT ONE ALWAYS CRACKS ME UP!

IT'S A CLASSIC!

ANDY CAPP

FLO'S STILL NOT TALKING TO ME

RUBY'S THE SAME WITH ME

I DON'T KNOW WHY THEY'RE SO UPSET— WE WERE ONLY PLAYING CARDS

I KNOW!

AND WE PUT THEM AWAY DURING THE VICAR'S EULOGY

EXACTLY!

ROGER MAHONEY & ROGER KETTLE

ANDY CAPP

I MUST ADMIT, HE HAS A REALLY STRESSFUL EXISTENCE

LIVING DAY-TO-DAY, NEVER KNOWING IF HE'S GOING TO ACCIDENTALLY ROLL OFF THE COUCH

ROGER MAHONEY & ROGER KETTLE

ANDY CAPP

WHAT FLO SAID TO ME BEFORE SHE WENT TO WORK WAS REALLY HURTFUL

DOES SHE REALLY BELIEVE I'M THE LAZIEST MAN WHO EVER LIVED?

I'LL SPEAK TO HER WHEN SHE GETS HOME AT FIVE — I'LL SET MY ALARM

ROGER MAHONEY & ROGER KETTLE

ANDY CAPP

DO YOU REALISE IT'S NEARLY TWELVE O'CLOCK?

GET OUT OF BED AND COME DOWNSTAIRS IMMEDIATELY!

THE COUCH IS WONDERING WHERE YOU'VE GOT TO! HEH! HEH!

SHE'S OBVIOUSLY BEEN WORKING ON THAT ONE FOR A WHILE

ROGER MAHONEY & ROGER KETTLE

ANDY CAPP

THERE ARE DEFINITELY ASPECTS OF THE GAME THAT ANDY HAS IMPROVED AT AS HE GETS OLDER

HE PANTS BETTER

PANT PANT

ROGER MAHONEY & ROGER KETTLE

ANDY CAPP

TCH! LOOK AT THE STATE OF THIS GARDEN — IT'S AN ABSOLUTE MESS!

WHERE DO I START?

DO I JUST COME STRAIGHT OUT AND ASK FLO TO DO IT? DO I DROP HER A FEW HINTS?

ROGER MAHONEY & ROGER KETTLE

ANDY CAPP

I'VE COME BACK TO YOU, PET — A CHANGED AND WISER MAN

FROM THIS MOMENT, I PROMISE TO BE MORE CONSIDERATE

TAKE JUST NOW, FOR EXAMPLE — I'LL WATCH T.V. WHILE YOU MAKE MY DINNER BUT I'LL KEEP THE SOUND DOWN

ROGER MAHONEY & ROGER KETTLE

ANDY CAPP

ANOTHER LOAN? WHAT HAPPENED TO THE MONEY I GAVE YOU YESTERDAY?

YOU KNOW HOW IT IS, PET — HOW FAR DOES MONEY GO THESE DAYS?

IN YOUR CASE, ABOUT SIX FURLONGS

ROGER MAHONEY & ROGER KETTLE

ANDY CAPP

 THERE WAS A NEW STYLIST AT THE HAIRDRESSER'S TODAY

 WELL, WHAT DO YOU THINK?

 TO CUT A LONG STORY SHORT, "YOU LOOK LIKE AN ELECTRIFIED POODLE" MEANS THAT I'M EATING IN HERE TONIGHT

ROGER MAHONEY & ROGER KETTLE

ANDY CAPP

 ANY CHANCE OF SOME DINNER IN HERE?

 SORRY ABOUT THAT, RUBE — HE'S A BIT GRUMPY AT THE MOMENT

 HE HASN'T SLEPT A WINK ALL AFTERNOON

ROGER MAHONEY & ROGER KETTLE

ANDY CAPP

 SO WHAT IF I'M LATE? I'M NOT SCARED OF MY WIFE / GOOD FOR YOU

 YEAH, SO WHAT IF I'M LATE? I'M NOT SCARED OF MY WIFE / YOU SAID THAT

 SO WHAT IF I'M LATE? I'M NOT SCARED OF MY WIFE! / YOU'RE GETTING HYSTERICAL—I'M GOING TO HAVE TO SLAP YOU

ROGER MAHONEY & ROGER KETTLE

ANDY CAPP

 I NEVER KNOW WHAT TO CALL YOUR MOTHER

 USING HER FIRST NAME SEEMS DISRESPECTFUL AND "MOTHER-IN-LAW" IS TOO MUCH OF A MOUTHFUL

 AND YET YOU'RE COMFORTABLE WITH "BEELZEBUB'S SISTER"

ROGER MAHONEY & ROGER KETTLE

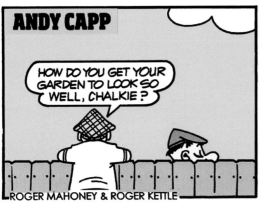

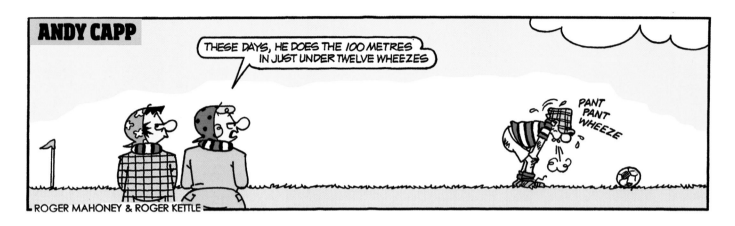

ANDY CAPP

POOR THING — HE'S EXHAUSTED

HIS ELECTRIC TOOTHBRUSH IS BROKEN — HE HAD TO BRUSH MANUALLY THIS MORNING

ROGER MAHONEY & ROGER KETTLE

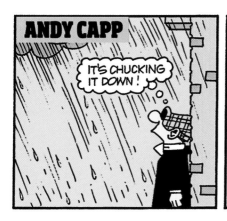

ANDY CAPP

THERE'S A REALLY NICE COUCH IN THAT SALE — IT WOULD LOOK GREAT IN OUR LIVING ROOM

SALE

OF COURSE, IF WE *DID* BUY IT, I'D HAVE TO HAVE A WORD WITH THE DELIVERY MEN

YOU KNOW, TO SEE IF THEY COULD FLIP YOU FROM THE OLD ONE TO THE NEW ONE WITHOUT WAKING YOU

ROGER MAHONEY & ROGER KETTLE

ANDY CAPP

HOW CAN I POSSIBLY GET HOME BEFORE MIDNIGHT? THE PUB DOESN'T SHUT TILL ONE!

HAS IT NEVER OCCURRED TO YOU THAT YOU COULD ACTUALLY LEAVE THE PUB *EARLY?*

WE'LL TALK ABOUT THIS IN THE MORNING — YOU'RE MAKING NO SENSE WHATEVER AT THE MOMENT

ROGER MAHONEY & ROGER KETTLE

ANDY CAPP

THE SMITHS ACROSS THE STREET ARE HAVING ANOTHER ROW

SHE'S JUST CALLED HIM "AS USELESS AS A BRICK PARACHUTE"

THIS IS GOLD DUST— I NEED A PEN AND PAPER!

ROGER MAHONEY & ROGER KETTLE

ANDY CAPP

MY WEDDING DRESS ARRIVED YESTERDAY — IT'S PERFECT

JOHN WANTS TO SEE IT BUT I TOLD HIM HE HAS TO WAIT FOR THE BIG DAY

AT LEAST HE CARES

ANDY WASN'T INTERESTED IN MINE — THE ONLY WAY HE'D HAVE SEEN IT BEFORE THE WEDDING IS IF THE BARMAN IN HIS LOCAL HAD WORN IT

ROGER MAHONEY & ROGER KETTLE

ANDY CAPP

I'M HOME, PET— WHAT A DAY I'VE HAD

NOT AS BAD AS MINE

THERE'S BEEN A FLY BUZZING AROUND IN HERE — I'VE HARDLY SLEPT A WINK ALL AFTERNOON

YES, THAT REALLY PUTS MY NINE-HOUR SHIFT AT WORK IN THE SHADE

ROGER MAHONEY & ROGER KETTLE

ANDY CAPP

READY TO GO TO THE PUB, ANDY?

FLO NEEDS A HAND MOVING A WARDROBE — I'LL SEE YOU DOWN THERE IN TEN MINUTES

I'LL HAVE A DRINK WAITING FOR YOU

ROGER MAHONEY & ROGER KETTLE

ANDY CAPP

MOST EVENINGS, TERRY AND I JUST SIT AND TALK

I CAN'T SAY THAT ANDY IS MUCH OF A CONVERSATIONALIST

IN FACT, I DON'T RECALL HIM USING TOO MANY SENTENCES THAT DON'T INCLUDE THE WORDS "FETCH", "BEER" AND "FRIDGE"

ROGER MAHONEY & ROGER KETTLE

ANDY CAPP

THAT'S BETTER, PET— YOU KEPT YOUR WRIST NICE AND STIFF UNTIL THE POINT OF RELEASE

NOW SMILE NICELY AT THE MAN WHILE I GO AND GET YOUR DART OUT OF HIS PINT

ROGER MAHONEY & ROGER KETTLE

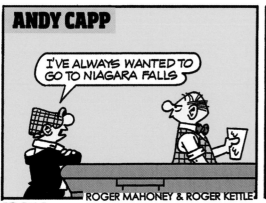

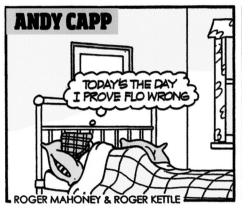

ANDY CAPP

I'M JUST GOING OUT FOR A QUICK PINT — I'LL BE BACK AT EIGHT FOR MY DINNER

OKAY

LAMB CHOPS OR FISH AND CHIPS? WHICH OF THESE WOULD YOU LIKE ME TO THROW IN THE BIN AT MIDNIGHT?

ROGER MAHONEY & ROGER KETTLE

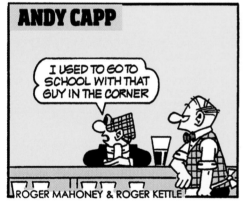

ANDY CAPP

THERE WAS A NEW STYLIST AT THE HAIRDRESSER'S TODAY

ROGER MAHONEY & ROGER KETTLE

SHE SUGGESTED WE DO SOMETHING DIFFERENT WITH MY HAIR

ENTER IT IN A "STUPID STYLE" CONTEST?

ANDY CAPP

WHAT DO YOU THINK OF MY NEW DRESS, PET? THEY SAY VERTICAL LINES MAKE A PERSON LOOK SLIMMER

ROGER MAHONEY & ROGER KETTLE

THE WORDS "THEY LIE" WERE OUT OF MY MOUTH BEFORE I COULD STOP THEM

ANDY CAPP

WELL, DID YOU CUT THE GRASS, LIKE I ASKED YOU TO?

ROGER MAHONEY & ROGER KETTLE

BEFORE I ANSWER THAT, WHAT ARE THE CHANCES OF YOU *NOT* GOING OUTSIDE TO CHECK?

ZERO

THEN, NO

ANDY CAPP

WE NEED A GOOD EXCUSE FOR BEING LATE

ROGER MAHONEY & ROGER KETTLE

WE COULD SAY THAT THE POLICE SEALED OFF THE TOWN CENTRE BECAUSE A TYRANNOSAURUS REX WAS RAMPAGING THROUGH THE STREETS

OR WE COULD SAY WE MISSED THE BUS

THAT'S PROBABLY BETTER

ANDY CAPP

SO WHAT DID YOU GET UP TO TODAY?

AFTER YOU LEFT THIS MORNING, I WALKED ALL OVER TOWN TRYING TO FIND A JOB FOR MYSELF

OH YOU POOR THING...

...YOU MUST BE EXHAUSTED AFTER ALL THAT LYING

ROGER MAHONEY & ROGER KETTLE

ANDY CAPP

ANY CHANCE OF SOME BREAKFAST, PET?

I'M ON MY WAY TO WORK! THERE ARE EGGS AND BACON IN THE FRIDGE — MAKE YOUR OWN BREAFAST!

NO, SERIOUSLY

ROGER MAHONEY & ROGER KETTLE

ANDY CAPP

MARRIAGE GUIDANCE

I DON'T KNOW WHY WE KEEP COMING HERE — OUR RELATIONSHIP IS FINE

MARRIAGE GUIDAN

MAYBE IT'S —

I'M TALKING!

ROGER MAHONEY & ROGER KETTLE

ANDY CAPP

I'LL COME BACK TO YOU WHEN YOU STOP TREATING ME LIKE YOUR PERSONAL SERVANT

COME BACK, PET — I WOULD NEVER TREAT YOU LIKE THAT!

HAVE YOU LEFT ANYTHING IN THE OVEN FOR ME?

ROGER MAHONEY & ROGER KETTLE

ANDY CAPP

THIS PARK IS SUCH A QUIET AND PEACEFUL PLACE

IT'S JUST LIKE BEING IN THE MIDDLE OF THE COUNTRYSIDE

ANY CHANCE OF GOING SOMEWHERE THAT'S JUST LIKE BEING IN THE MIDDLE OF A PUB?

ROGER MAHONEY & ROGER KETTLE

ANDY CAPP

I DON'T KNOW HOW I GOT THROUGH WORK TODAY— I'VE GOT A SPLITTING HEADACHE AND I'M CHOKED WITH THE COLD

HAVE WE GOT ANY OTHER CUSHIONS, PET? THIS ONE MAKES LINES ON MY FACE

THERE'S ALWAYS SOMEONE WORSE OFF THAN YOURSELF

ROGER MAHONEY & ROGER KETTLE

ANDY CAPP

I WAS THINKING BACK TO OUR WEDDING RECEPTION

REMEMBER HOW MY RELATIVES WERE SITTING ON ONE SIDE OF THE ROOM AND YOUR RELATIVES ON THE OTHER?

YES

WHO THREW THE FIRST BOTTLE?

IT WAS NEVER ESTABLISHED

ROGER MAHONEY & ROGER KETTLE

ANDY CAPP

WHAT I NEED IS A STRONG MAN....

...A STRONG, POWERFUL MAN WHO WILL PROTECT ME AND TAKE CARE OF ME

I CAN'T GET THE LID OFF THE JAM, PET

ROGER MAHONEY & ROGER KETTLE

OTHER CLASSIC STRIPS

Modesty Blaise: Sweet Caroline
ISBN: 9781848566736

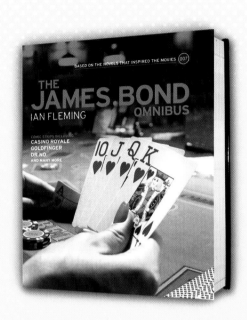

The James Bond Omnibus: (Vol. 001)
ISBN: 9781848563643

The Misadventures of Jane
ISBN: 9781848561670

Beetle Bailey:
The Daily & Sunday Strips 1965
ISBN: 9781848567061

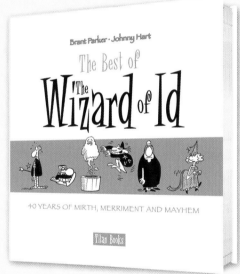

Wizard of Id:
The Best of the Wizard of Id
ISBN: 9781848563636

The Epic Chronicles of Hägar the
Horrible: The Dailies (1974–75)
ISBN: 9781848562349

AVAILABLE NOW
FROM TITAN BOOKS